grade

# 3

For full details of exam requirements, please refer to the current syllabus in conjunction with *Examination Information & Regulations* and the guide for candidates, teachers and parents, *These Music Exams*. These three documents are available online at www.abrsm.org, as well as free of charge from music retailers, from ABRSM local representatives or from the Services Department, The Associated Board of the Royal Schools of Music, 24 Portland Place, London W1B 1LU, United Kingdom.

## CONTENTS



Where appropriate, pieces in this album have been checked with original source material and edited as necessary for instructional purposes. Fingering, bowing, composers' metronome marks and the editorial realization of ornaments (where given) are for guidance only; they are not comprehensive or obligatory. Metronome marks within square brackets are suggested for exam purposes and need not be strictly observed.

Violin consultant: Edward Huws Jones
Footnotes: Edward Huws Jones (EHJ) and Anthony Burton

Alternative pieces for this grade

LIST A

4 **Gossec** Gavotte. No. 17 from *Suzuki Violin School*, Vol. 1 (Summy-Birchard/Faber)
5 **Jacques Hotteterre** Gavotte (la Meudon). *Baroque Violinist*, ed. Nelson (Boosey & Hawkes/MDS)
6 **Pachelbel** Canon. *The Classic Experience – Violin*, arr. Lanning (Cramer)

LIST B

4 **Piazzolla** Chiquilín de Bachín (violin melody). *The Tango Fiddler*, arr. Huws Jones (Boosey & Hawkes/MDS)
5 **Schumann** The Two Grenadiers (Op. 49 No. 1). No. 7 from *Suzuki Violin School*, Vol. 2 (Summy-Birchard/Faber)
6 **David Stone** Berceuse: No. 5 from *Eight Pieces in the Third Position* (Novello/Music Sales)

LIST C

4 **W. Kroll** Donkey Doodle. *Solos for Young Violinists*, Vol. 1, ed. Barber (Summy-Birchard/Faber)
5 **Szelényi** The Little Chatter-Box: No. 8 from *24 Easy Little Concert Pieces*, Vol. 1 (Editio Musica Budapest/Faber)
6 **Trad. Mexican** La Cucaracha. *Abracadabra Violin*, Book 2, arr. Alexander (Black)



Music origination by Barnes Music Engraving Ltd
Cover by Økvik Design
Printed in England by Caligraving Ltd, Thetford, Norfolk

# Lord Cutt's March

Edited and continuo realization by
Philip Ledger

ANON.

*Lord Cutt's March* comes from a series called Warlike Musick, described as 'a Choice Collection of Marches & Trumpet Tunes for a German Flute, Violin or Harpsicord [sic] by Mr. HANDEL, St. MARTINI and the most Eminent Masters'. The series was printed by Handel's regular London publisher John Walsh in 1760 – which, as the editor Philip Ledger points out, was a time of intense military activity in Europe and North America. The tune is not by Handel or Sammartini, nor as far as we know by any 'Eminent Master', as claimed by the publisher. It may be associated with Lord Cutt's Regiment of Foot, which formed part of the British Army for a short period from 1674. In the violin melody, enjoy the trumpet-like repeated quavers, which need to be played on the string but fairly staccato. The slurs, dynamics and articulation are suggestions for exam purposes and may be varied. The trill in b. 17 is editorial. The final trill can be played using the open string, as was often the practice in Baroque music.

# Lady Hunsdon's Puffe

A:2

Arranged by
Edward Huws Jones

DOWLAND

John Dowland (1563–1626) was the most celebrated lutenist of his time and *Lady Hunsdon's Puffe* was originally written as a lute solo. The Hunsdon family were noted patrons of the arts and Dowland may even have been employed by them early in his career. This piece is in the rhythm of an almain, a dance which often had military connotations; it should be played in a forthright style, rather like a march. The 'puffe' in the title means proud or boastful, as in the modern phrase 'puffed up'. EHJ

# German Dance

WoO 8 No. 1

Arranged by
Paul de Keyser and Fanny Waterman

BEETHOVEN

Ludwig van Beethoven (1770–1827) is best known as the composer of powerfully dramatic symphonies, concertos, string quartets and so on. But, like most composers of his time, he also wrote a good deal of light music for practical use. This is the first of a set of a dozen German Dances for orchestra which he composed for a masked ball in Vienna in November 1795; they were published in versions for piano and for two violins and cello. The German Dance was the name given in the late 18th and early 19th centuries to a dance for couples in triple time; the term was later replaced by the more specific titles of ländler and waltz. In the first half of the piece, much of the character comes from lifting the bow on the staccato crotchet at the beginning of bb. 1, 3, 5 and 6 etc. The second half is more legato and would benefit from a little crescendo through each of the rising quaver scales.

# Grande valse brillante

B:1

Op. 18

Arranged by
Mary Cohen

CHOPIN

Fryderyk Franciszek Chopin (1810–49) was Polish by birth but spent most of his adult life in France. He wrote almost entirely for his own instrument, the piano, chiefly in sets of smaller pieces, many of them in dance rhythms. This is a simplified arrangement of the opening part of his well-known Waltz in E flat major, Op. 18, written in 1831 and published three years later – his first waltz to appear in print – with the title *Grande valse brillante* and a dedication to his pupil Laura Horsford.

# B:2 Jeanie with the Light Brown Hair

Arranged by
Jerry Lanning

S. FOSTER

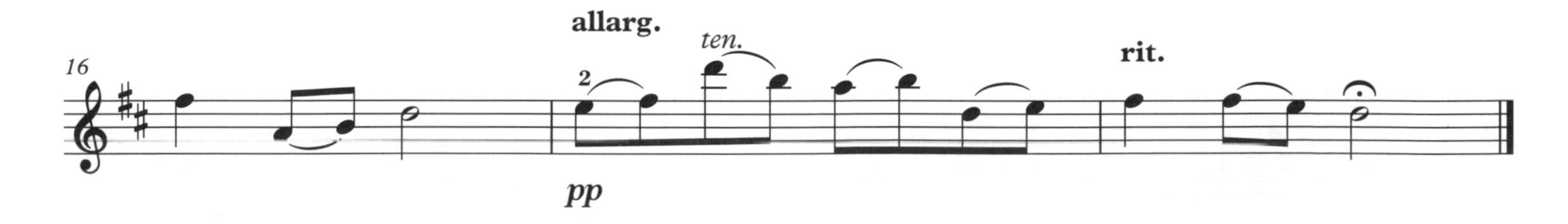


Stephen Foster (1826–64) was the first great American songwriter, responsible for such familiar songs as *Camptown Races*, *Old Folks at Home* and *Beautiful Dreamer*. This one was written in 1854 in honour of his wife Jane McDowell, and begins:

  I dream of Jeanie with the light brown hair,
  Borne, like a vapor, on the summer air...

It is a sentimental love song, which needs to be played expressively rather than too 'cleanly'.

grade

# 3 Violin exam pieces

Piano accompaniment

For full details of exam requirements, please refer to the current syllabus in conjunction with *Examination Information & Regulations* and the guide for candidates, teachers and parents, *These Music Exams*. These three documents are available online at www.abrsm.org, as well as free of charge from music retailers, from ABRSM local representatives or from the Services Department, The Associated Board of the Royal Schools of Music, 24 Portland Place, London W1B 1LU, United Kingdom.

## REQUIREMENTS

SCALES AND ARPEGGIOS (from memory)
in E major; E minor (one octave)
G, A, B♭, D majors; G, A, D minors (two octaves)

**Scales**
in the above keys (minors in melodic *or* harmonic form at candidate's choice):
(i) separate bows
(ii) slurred, two quavers to a bow

**Chromatic Scales**
starting on open strings G, D and A (one octave):
separate bows, even notes

**Arpeggios**
the common chords of the above keys:
(i) separate bows, even notes
(ii) slurred, three notes to a bow

**Dominant Sevenths**
in the keys of C, G and D (starting on open strings G, D and A and resolving on the tonic) (one octave):
separate bows, even notes

PLAYING AT SIGHT (see current syllabus)

AURAL TESTS (see current syllabus)

THREE PIECES *page*



Candidates must prepare three pieces, one from each of the three Lists, A, B and C. Candidates may choose from the pieces printed in this album or any other piece listed for the grade. A full list is given in the current syllabus.


Violin consultant:
Edward Huws Jones
Footnotes:
Edward Huws Jones (EHJ)
and Anthony Burton

Music origination by Barnes Music Engraving Ltd

Cover by Økvik Design

Printed in England by Caligraving Ltd, Thetford, Norfolk


Where appropriate, pieces in this album have been checked with original source material and edited as necessary for instructional purposes. Fingering, bowing, composers' metronome marks and the editorial realization of ornaments (where given) are for guidance only; they are not comprehensive or obligatory. Metronome marks within square brackets are suggested for exam purposes and need not be strictly observed.

# Lord Cutt's March

Edited and continuo realization by
Philip Ledger

ANON.

*Lord Cutt's March* comes from a series called Warlike Musick, described as 'a Choice Collection of Marches & Trumpet Tunes for a German Flute, Violin or Harpsicord [sic] by Mr. HANDEL, St. MARTINI and the most Eminent Masters'. The series was printed by Handel's regular London publisher John Walsh in 1760 – which, as the editor Philip Ledger points out, was a time of intense military activity in Europe and North America. The tune is not by Handel or Sammartini, nor as far as we know by any 'Eminent Master', as claimed by the publisher. It may be associated with Lord Cutt's Regiment of Foot, which formed part of the British Army for a short period from 1674. In the violin melody, enjoy the trumpet-like repeated quavers, which need to be played on the string but fairly staccato. The slurs, dynamics and articulation are suggestions for exam purposes and may be varied. The trill in b. 17 is editorial. The final trill can be played using the open string, as was often the practice in Baroque music.

13
mf
mf

16
tr
p
p

20
cresc.
tr
f
mf
cresc.
f
mf

# Lady Hunsdon's Puffe

Arranged by
Edward Huws Jones

DOWLAND

John Dowland (1563–1626) was the most celebrated lutenist of his time and *Lady Hunsdon's Puffe* was originally written as a lute solo. The Hunsdon family were noted patrons of the arts and Dowland may even have been employed by them early in his career. This piece is in the rhythm of an almain, a dance which often had military connotations; it should be played in a forthright style, rather like a march. The 'puffe' in the title means proud or boastful, as in the modern phrase 'puffed up'. EHJ

12
p
p

15
1
f
0
mf
f
mf

19
4
0
4
cresc.
f
cresc.
f

# German Dance

WoO 8 No. 1

Arranged by
Paul de Keyser and Fanny Waterman

BEETHOVEN

Ludwig van Beethoven (1770–1827) is best known as the composer of powerfully dramatic symphonies, concertos, string quartets and so on. But, like most composers of his time, he also wrote a good deal of light music for practical use. This is the first of a set of a dozen German Dances for orchestra which he composed for a masked ball in Vienna in November 1795; they were published in versions for piano and for two violins and cello. The German Dance was the name given in the late 18th and early 19th centuries to a dance for couples in triple time; the term was later replaced by the more specific titles of ländler and waltz. In the first half of the piece, much of the character comes from lifting the bow on the staccato crotchet at the beginning of bb. 1, 3, 5 and 6 etc. The second half is more legato and would benefit from a little crescendo through each of the rising quaver scales.

# Grande valse brillante

B:1

Op. 18

Arranged by
Mary Cohen

CHOPIN

Fryderyk Franciszek Chopin (1810–49) was Polish by birth but spent most of his adult life in France. He wrote almost entirely for his own instrument, the piano, chiefly in sets of smaller pieces, many of them in dance rhythms. This is a simplified arrangement of the opening part of his well-known Waltz in E flat major, Op. 18, written in 1831 and published three years later – his first waltz to appear in print – with the title *Grande valse brillante* and a dedication to his pupil Laura Horsford.

17
p leggiero
pp leggiero
22
26
30

35
f
mf
40
dim.
dim.
44
p cresc.
pp cresc.
f
mf
49

# B:2 Jeanie with the Light Brown Hair

Arranged by
Jerry Lanning

S. FOSTER

Stephen Foster (1826–64) was the first great American songwriter, responsible for such familiar songs as *Camptown Races, Old Folks at Home* and *Beautiful Dreamer*. This one was written in 1854 in honour of his wife Jane McDowell, and begins:

I dream of Jeanie with the light brown hair,
Borne, like a vapor, on the summer air…

It is a sentimental love song, which needs to be played expressively rather than too 'cleanly'.

10
2
3

13
2
mf
dim.
0
2
p
mf
dim.
p

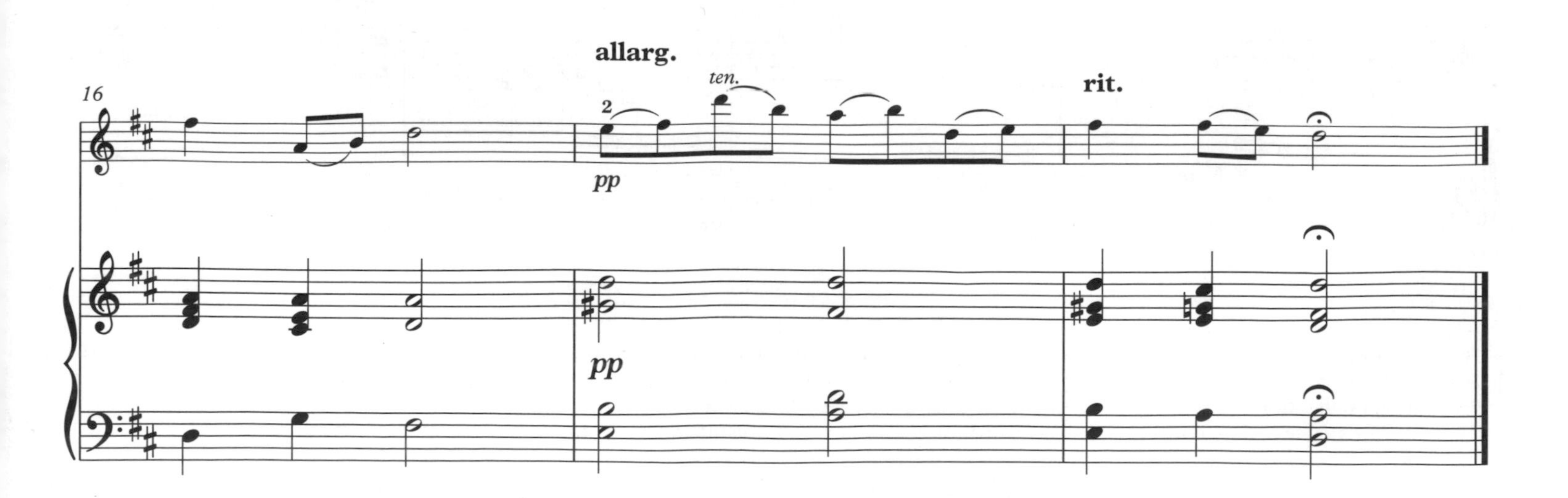
allarg.
16
2
ten.
rit.
pp
pp

B:3

# O mio babbino caro

from *Gianni Schicchi*

Arranged by
Jerry Lanning

G. PUCCINI

The only comedy among the operas of the Italian composer Giacomo Puccini (1858–1924) is *Gianni Schicchi*, the final component of his 1918 *Trittico* or triptych of one-act pieces. This famous short aria *O mio babbino caro*, or 'O my beloved Daddy', is not quite the straightforward declaration of affection the title suggests: the singer is actually trying to extract a favour from her father. The tempo direction *Andante ingenuo* means 'a little slowly and ingenuously', in other words pretending to be innocent; *dolce e legato* means 'sweetly and smoothly'.

12
p
p
16
p
p
19
pp
ten.
pp
ten.
p
23
rit.
pp
pp

Blank page

# Old Joe Clark

Arranged by
Polly Waterfield and Louise Beach

ANON.

Old Joe Clark seems to have been a real person, who lived in the mountains of Clay County, Kentucky, in the mid-19th century. His friends (and enemies) started making up verses about him during his lifetime, to fit an existing instrumental tune, and the resulting ballad was sung by Kentucky soldiers in the First World War and printed in various versions from 1918 onwards. One of the verses, with chorus, is as follows:

Old Joe Clark he had a house/Forty storeys high/And every storey in that house/Was lined with chicken pie.

Fare you well, old Joe Clark/Fare you well I say/Fare you well, old Joe Clark/For I'm a-goin' away.

You might imagine the tune, and the variations on it, being played by a country fiddler and a banjo player. Notice that the tune is modal: although the keynote is E, the key signature is only three sharps, so all the Ds (except for a couple of grace notes) are D naturals.

Variation 1
p
mp
p leggiero
(LH pizz.)
mf
(arco)
mf
mp
f
1.
mp
f

Variation 2
36b
2.
f
mf
poco dim.
sim.
41
46
51
p
cresc.
ff

# Sweet Lorraine

Arranged by
Edward Huws Jones

BURWELL and PARISH

*Sweet Lorraine* is a classic jazz tune from the 1920s. It should be performed in an easy swing rhythm. If you want to become more familiar with the style, listen to some of the great jazz violinists such as Joe Venuti, who recorded the piece in 1933. EHJ

Music by Clifford Burwell Words by Mitchell Parish

17
22
27
31
f
p
mf

# Rumba

No. 4 from *A Sketchbook for Violin*

MICHAEL ROSE

Michael Rose (b. 1934) studied at the Royal Academy of Music and later worked for the BBC and as music advisor for a number of borough councils. He has composed extensively for various instruments and is also a teacher and conductor. The rumba is a Cuban dance, danced with swaying hips to a characteristic Latin-American rhythm. For most of the piece, each bar is divided not into four equal beats but into groups of 3, 3 and 2 quavers. But the piano part gets more complicated than that at times, and towards the end, while the piano maintains the 3+3+2 rhythm, the violin plays a counter-melody in 4/4 time. You will need to repeat the main rhythmic pattern until you feel entirely at ease with it, so that you can achieve the relaxation suggested by the tempo marking of 'moderate and agreeable'. You could use open A strings in this piece, to make a ringing, open sound.

12
16
mf
19
22
mf

senza rit.

# O mio babbino caro

B:3

from *Gianni Schicchi*

Arranged by
Jerry Lanning

G. PUCCINI

The only comedy among the operas of the Italian composer Giacomo Puccini (1858–1924) is *Gianni Schicchi*, the final component of his 1918 *Trittico* or triptych of one-act pieces. This famous short aria *O mio babbino caro*, or 'O my beloved Daddy', is not quite the straightforward declaration of affection the title suggests: the singer is actually trying to extract a favour from her father. The tempo direction *Andante ingenuo* means 'a little slowly and ingenuously', in other words pretending to be innocent; *dolce e legato* means 'sweetly and smoothly'.

# Old Joe Clark

Arranged by
Polly Waterfield and Louise Beach

ANON.

Old Joe Clark seems to have been a real person, who lived in the mountains of Clay County, Kentucky, in the mid-19th century. His friends (and enemies) started making up verses about him during his lifetime, to fit an existing instrumental tune, and the resulting ballad was sung by Kentucky soldiers in the First World War and printed in various versions from 1918 onwards. One of the verses, with chorus, is as follows:

Old Joe Clark he had a house/Forty storeys high/And every storey in that house/Was lined with chicken pie.

Fare you well, old Joe Clark/Fare you well I say/Fare you well, old Joe Clark/For I'm a-goin' away.

You might imagine the tune, and the variations on it, being played by a country fiddler and a banjo player. Notice that the tune is modal: although the keynote is E, the key signature is only three sharps, so all the Ds (except for a couple of grace notes) are D naturals.

# Sweet Lorraine

C:2

Arranged by
Edward Huws Jones

BURWELL and PARISH

*Sweet Lorraine* is a classic jazz tune from the 1920s. It should be performed in an easy swing rhythm. If you want to become more familiar with the style, listen to some of the great jazz violinists such as Joe Venuti, who recorded the piece in 1933. EHJ

Music by Clifford Burwell  Words by Mitchell Parish

# Rumba

No. 4 from *A Sketchbook for Violin*

MICHAEL ROSE

Michael Rose (b. 1934) studied at the Royal Academy of Music and later worked for the BBC and as music advisor for a number of borough councils. He has composed extensively for various instruments and is also a teacher and conductor. The rumba is a Cuban dance, danced with swaying hips to a characteristic Latin-American rhythm. For most of the piece, each bar is divided not into four equal beats but into groups of 3, 3 and 2 quavers. But the piano part gets more complicated than that at times, and towards the end, while the piano maintains the 3+3+2 rhythm, the violin plays a counter-melody in 4/4 time. You will need to repeat the main rhythmic pattern until you feel entirely at ease with it, so that you can achieve the relaxation suggested by the tempo marking of 'moderate and agreeable'. You could use open A strings in this piece, to make a ringing, open sound.